SACRED QUEST

SACRED QUEST

... through the Mountains of Northern New Mexico

By Elizabeth Schultze

EMAIL: sacredquest.sf@gmail.com

www.ElizabethSchultze.com

"The privilege of a lifetime
is to become
who you truly are."
Carl Jung

This book is dedicated to my family and friends
who have helped me discover my true self,
and to Forrest Fenn who gave all of us
the Adventure of a Lifetime.

Preface

In 2010 Art Collector/Author/Former Air Force Pilot, Forrest Fenn, hid a treasure chest filled with gold coins and other valuables estimated to be worth at least one million dollars. He hid it "in the mountains north of Santa Fe." According to Fenn, the chest weighed about 22 pounds and its dimensions were 10" x 10" x 5".

To locate the treasure, the finder would have to solve the cryptic 24-line poem included in his 2010 memoir, *The Thrill of the Chase*. The memoir recalled many of Fenn's life experiences including his time in the United States Air Force as a pilot during the Vietnam war. He wrote about events in his life that led him to understanding one of life's mysteries – Why are we here?

In addition, Fenn said that the book contained hints to finding the chest. Over the years, Fenn suggested that the loot was hid in a place that was special to him.

I learned about *The Thrill of the Chase* on a February morning in 2013. Here is my story.

Elizabeth Schultze (Moon Shadow)

Table of Contents

THE HERO'S JOURNEY

PART I – The Beginning

PART II – The Adventures

THE HERO's JOURNEY

The Characters

Hero...Moon Shadow

Mentor...Old Man

Herald..My Oldest Son

Ally...Great Spirit

Trickster.. Secret Language

Shapeshifter.....................................Sacred Animals

Guardian..Butterfly Maiden

Shadow..Doubt

PART 1 – The Beginning

My Ordinary World

Call to Adventure

Meeting the Mentor

Crossing the Threshold

My Ordinary World

The traditional life of a woman is ordinary. It consists of work, family, home, and friends. Although this life is full of love, joy and surprises, there are moments when a woman wants something more, something extraordinary, something remarkable, . . . An adventure!

My adventure began on a cold February morning in the year 2013 the day after leaving a part-time job that lacked, well it lacked everything.

Call to Adventure

The cold, crisp February morning was full of getting everyone to school. As I retreated to my bedroom, I contemplated what I would do next in life.

Out of the blue my oldest son came to me and heralded: "You are destined for greatness!" I smiled at him and reflected on how he said the most profound things. I pondered for a few moments the possible significance of those words.

In the next few moments, a vision came to me.[1] An Old Man appeared and began talking about a treasure 🧰 he had hidden "in the mountains somewhere north of Santa Fe".[2] He invited everyone to join the adventure. Knowing that only one would finish the journey he looked straight at me and said, "It is waiting just for you."

The vision faded away and I was stunned. A hidden treasure! That does not happen in real life! I soon discovered it did. It was true. And this man in my vision would assist me along the way.

Before I knew it, his

BOOK

OF SECRETS

was in my hands.[3]

Meeting the Mentor

Many of those on this same journey had met with the Old Man. I wanted to meet him too. While reading his 📖, I felt so close to him. I felt like I knew him already – heart to heart. When my father came to visit in May, I took the opportunity to ask the Old Man if we could visit him. Both he and my father had been in the Service of the Iron Birds during their younger years.[4] The Old Man gladly accepted my request.

My entire family traveled to his dwelling and met with him in his secret cave.[5] My heart did double flips as I met him in person. The Old Man had an unforgettable twinkle in his eyes. His hair was white as sand, his eyes as BLUE as the Caribbean Sea. He unveiled his great collections and talked with us about his own journey.

The Old Man shared tales of his days in Service of the Iron Birds. He took us inside his secret vault which displayed his first arrowhead and others, rifles, and other objects sacred to him.

We marveled at both his words and his sacred items.

"Life is a game of poker,
Happiness is the pot.
Fate deals you four cards and a joker,
And you play whether you like it or not." [6]

As we sat with him and listened,

Time ...

did not exist.

Crossing the Threshold

It was not long after reading his 📖 that I embarked on my own journey to the 🧰. It would take me on wild adventures, where I would meet a multitude of characters who would guide me to become myself in a way I never knew possible. Each time I re-entered this odyssey, I stepped through a mystical portal that invigorated my experiences. This enchanted passageway unlocked every time I put on my old, tattered hat 🎩 and I remembered his words, "Imagination is more important than knowledge."[7]

Like the Old Man had once said, "Some stories must move at their own pace and in their own time."[8] This is one of them.

PART II – The Adventures

The Abandoned Ship

As I rode towards the ship marooned on an immense, unreachable cliff, I knew it guarded secrets of times long ago. [9] This ship defended the area below at the confluence of the Divine River and its East Fork. Water is rare in these parts.

As I meandered along one of the trails, I found myself lost in the charm of the path. Scattered boulders supported the sides of the trail and greenery sprouted everywhere. I stopped and listened to the gentle ripples of the stream and thought about the Old Man who loved the mountains. "The mountains continue to beckon me. They always will."[10]

I was awakened from my thoughts when I heard voices from above. As I listened closer, I heard the cries were of men in their last moments trying to save the ship from the sandbar: "Check your swing… Give her more helm… Hard over… Hard over…Nooooo!" And then silence.

The utterances lasted only a moment. I was not sure what this all meant, but I could hear the emotion and tension in their voices. I stood there for a moment lost in thought until the wind caught my 🎩 . I ran to catch it.

I continued to think about these brave men as I walked the trail looking for clues to the Old Man's . The memory of the sailors on that fateful day lingered in my mind.

The Water Circles

The journey to the water circles was long and confusing.[11] I stopped a man who was walking along the path and asked for directions. He told me I was close and then gave the remaining directives.

After tethering my black horse, Bandit, I put on my  and began the long walk down the switchback trail.[12] The drop down the canyon trail was steep and treacherous. I kept my steps cautious and sober. As I reached the bottom of the canyon, I realized these circles of water had been used by many long before me.

The Ancient Ones used these waters for healing. The waters were among numerous springs considered to be the fountain of youth. I had heard stories of a man trying to use these waters to his own selfish advantage.

As I approached the springs, I saw an old man sitting in the largest spring. He seemed to be talking to himself, so I sat in one of the smaller pools and could not help but listen.

"God damn it, what's wrong with these people. Don't they know this could be one of the country's greatest resorts? We can say that these damn warm waters are the Fountain of Youth! We could build a hotel and resort and charge exorbitant prices. We'd be millionaires in no time. All I need is a few damn fools to invest with me. God damn it. I have it all figured out. I just need some of their god damn money. This place is a gold mine!"

I knew the man was none other than Arthur Manby! The man who claimed the land as his own. He wanted to turn these hot springs into the "Lost Springs of the Ancient Ones." There he was sitting only a few feet from me! He was not well liked and always scheming to make money.

As I turned to look at him again, he was gone. Only a few of the bricks from his bathhouse were left. I sat and thought about this man. Across the Rio Grande I saw the traces of stagecoach trails zigzagging across the canyon. Their trails were disappearing into the black abyss.

I looked for the ... in the waters, along the walls of the canyon and under the wood in the river. Nothing. I came back several times to look for the among the water circles, but never found it.

I never saw Manby again either, but I thought about how his greed had led to his own demise.

The Forgotten Bridge

I decided to relocate my hunt up the Big River to the Iron Bridge.[13] It was a smoother, easier ride for Bandit. When we arrived, I tethered Bandit under the shade of a grand cottonwood and put on my .

I walked down the hill towards the location of the Iron Bridge, but the bridge was not there. I looked up the river and saw what I thought was a bridge, but it was not the one I was expecting. It was the original Wooden Bridge! How was this happening? The new Iron Bridge had disappeared, and the old Wooden Bridge was there!

As I peered under the bridge for the , a stagecoach approached from the other side of the river. A tall, thin man with an old cowboy hat was driving the coach. I snuck deeper under the bridge and waited for the stagecoach to cross. The morning had mysteriously changed to evening. The stagecoach halted on the bridge.

I heard the old cowboy tell the folks, "It's too late in the day to continue. We must spend the night at the hotel. It's up yonder." I looked, and yes, there was a small hotel on the corner of the gorge's wall. They continued and stopped in front of the hotel. A man and a woman stepped off the stagecoach and entered the building.

That old man must be the real Long John Dunn. I had heard stories about him. He was a sneaky old man. He owned the only stagecoach that ran from the train west of the Big River to the Artist Village.[14] He was the only show in town. He managed to always include a stop at his hotel to make more money off these poor folks whose only desire was to get to the Artist Village.

I fell asleep under the bridge as the candles dimmed in the hotel. In the morning's light I walked back to Bandit. I had seen Long John Dunn! What a treasure to see the man who had helped make the Artist Village flourish. I did not find the chest there, but I discovered and learned so much about Long John Dunn and the history of the old Artist Village.

The Old Artist Village

The Sparkling Waterfall

In time, I decided that the chest was not to be found in the land of Long John Dunn. I had searched in places all over that area and came to believe the Old Man had not hidden it there. I began looking a bit closer to home. I heard about a beautiful waterfall just north of the Old City.[15] I stumbled upon directions to it eventually. Many believed the chest was near a waterfall and this was the only one I knew about.

It was a warm October day when my younger son and I set out in search of the Sparkling Waterfall. We left Bandit at the beginning of the trail with water and an apple. We stepped onto the footpath and found ourselves traveling through the midst of a prismatic forest. The changing colors of crimson, gold, and coral enveloped us from above and below. The humble stream held the colors of fall as we traversed it. We had hiked only a short distance when a large white dog appeared and began leading us.

I told my son that this must be the Wolf Spirit in disguise. The wolf is a symbol of guardianship, loyalty, and spirit. He teaches us to trust our hearts and minds. If we put our trust in him, he would lead us to the waterfall.

It was obvious that the Wolf Spirit knew the way to the waterfall. He bolted ahead of us but would wait patiently if we fell behind. As we rested, the Wolf Spirit sat beside us. We shared our snack with him and in return he laid his head on my son's lap. When we returned to the journey, he sprang ahead again. We followed, full of trust.

Before we knew it, we turned a corner and there was the waterfall. The walls of the waterfall sparkled like diamonds. Although the water was freezing, my son braved the icy water to look behind the waterfall for the . He called out to me saying he could not find it.

When he emerged from the water, we sat on a large tree branch. We talked about the mystical presence in this small alcove. The Wolf Spirit stayed with us until it was time to leave. All the way home we talked about the Wolf Spirit who had kept us safe and led us to this enchanting, otherworldly place.

The Monastery on the River

As time continued and fall turned to winter, I spent time researching and contemplating where to search next. Time had been going by quickly. When an early spring arrived, I decided to search near the Monastery on the river.[16]

The thirteen-mile dusty ride to the Monastery was among the most breathtaking I had ever seen. Every turn contained a new view of brilliant, rich formations ranging in hues of maroon and creams to emeralds and chestnuts. The bumpy ride led to the feeling of truly being on a journey. With no one around for miles, I found myself alone with my thoughts. The allure of the landscape could not be resisted. Pure artistry surrounded me. Imagination burst among the elegant formations.

As I sauntered around the Monastery, I saw it for the first time. I found myself transported back to the time when Father Aelred Wall saw it the first time as well. He knew this was a holy place. I saw him walk among the lanky trees and the swaying willows toward the slow-moving, sparkling river. He knew he was meant to create a holy place for others.

"Yes, I walk upon this holy ground in prayer, knowing that my prayers are heard ... Be holy, because I am holy" (Lev 11.44, 45).

The tributary flowed before me in a soft, rippling motion. The mountains spoke of the glories of God. The Old Man had once told me, "My church is in the mountains and along the river bottoms where dreams and fantasies alike go to play."[17] Perhaps this was the Old Man's holy place.

I searched among the willows and along the river bottoms on countless occasions. I found myself traveling to this place even though I knew the  was not here. The place was sacred, and I wanted to walk on its holy ground.

The Frog Prince

I trekked to the hidden frog pond on a blustery, winter day. The roads were open, but the wind was frigid and crisp. I discovered the hidden pond among the gigantic fir trees. Large boulders surrounded and protected it. I listened quietly for the sounds of winter in the forest.[18] I had hoped to see some frogs but realized they might be hibernating.

I searched the edges of the pond for the , but found none. I decided to sit for a moment. As I squatted near the edge, I noticed that the trail had disappeared. I was alone in this magnificent forest, but not afraid. I felt at home and at peace. The fuzzy, brown cattails monopolized at least a quarter of the pond. As I gazed at them, I began to daydream.

I thought I saw some gold sparkling in the pond. I stood up to get a bit closer. Suddenly a golden frog jumped out of the pond and landed near me. I sat down again and looked at him with his bulbous eyes and long legs.

He spoke to me, "What are you looking for, precious one?"

I was stunned to hear him talk. I stuttered for a moment and then replied to him, "I am looking for the Old Man's Treasure. Have you heard of it?"

"Ah …. Yes, I have seen a few people in these woods, but they never take the time to stop and enjoy the pond. They walk quickly, glancing, and moving on." He continued, "Why have you stopped?"

I told him, "I was looking at the cattails. I have not seen any in so long. Then I started feeling at home here and didn't want to leave."

"Yes, you have found the true treasure … the wonder of nature. Time does not move forward when one ponders the enchantment of the land. Continue to find the delightfulness all around you."

"I will," I promised him. Then he leapt back into the pond and swam to the cattails where he disappeared. I sat there a long time thinking about what he had told me.

Among the Willows

My adventures continued to where the small creek brimming with willows met the River of Trading.[19] As I crept among the marshy ground through the willows looking for the [image], I found myself thinking about all those who had previously traveled through these marshes.

I advanced to the River of Trading and looked to the mountain east of me. I saw a stripped, barren hillside with a large mine on top of it. It looked incredibly sad to me.

I stumbled upon some boarding houses. I realized this must have been part of the old mining camp.[20] As I continued walking around the mining camp. I discovered more and more of the camp - a school, a hospital, restaurants, and a jail.

I stood behind the old schoolhouse as the sun disappeared behind the mountain. I heard the voices of the miners as they left work and headed for home.

The muscular miners appeared tired and dirty. They did not seem to notice me. I could hear only Spanish as I looked upon their blackened faces. "Lista para una cerveza y una mujer. Vamos a Chihuahua." My Spanish was not good, but it was good enough to know that they were ready for beer and women.

I had heard the red-light district was known as "Chihuahua." I followed them to the building they entered. Peeking in the window I saw men sitting around tables drinking. The women served them and flirted with them. I watched as one man took a woman's arm and led her through a back door.

It was deep into the night when I decided to head back. The morning light came as I neared Bandit. He was eating the tall grass. I looked back at the mountain. The mine was gone, the hills covered in meadows and trees. Everything had returned to its natural state.

We rode home in the morning's light as I thought about the men who worked so hard in this mine. I remembered what the Old Man had said in his book; there will be a time "where the past will come alive again and all of my experiences and friends through the years will meet with me at the great banquet table of history. Then there will be no past."[21]

Maybe for some of us the great banquet table will be in a bar or at a picnic table or simply on a blanket in the forest.

The Cave of Forgotten Memories

My expedition to the cave of forgotten memories became a hike through an enchanted forest.[22] Along the path were footprints of previous pilgrims. As I traipsed further into the depths of the forest, it became necessary to cross the winding stream over bridges of logs.

The spring flowers were bursting into full color. The long blades of grass flourished with tender sprouts. The shadows amongst the trees appeared as silhouettes of animals.

The path was worn, and I expected to meet others along the way. There were none. As I neared the cave, I grew excited. Caves are rare and to find one to be explored was magnificent!

The cave's opening resembled two big eyes. The wall in between the opening appeared to be a large nose. I explored the small cave. It was full of water, but I could walk close to the walls to get inside. It was intriguing! A skull of a coyote perched on a wall guarded the inside the cave. It spoke warnings about traveling too far inside.

As I sat outside the cave on a log, I found myself staring into its eyes. The cave spoke to me.

"The cave you fear to enter holds the treasure you seek."[23]

That was all it said. I knew I was on a spiritual journey within this  hunt and the cave's words stayed with me. I think about it often as I face my own fears.

The gift of the cave was profound.

The Hummingbird Man

On my birthday one year I asked my husband to join me on a walk down the River of Trading. Yes, I would be hunting along the way, but he would enjoy it also. We started our journey early that July morning to avoid the flies that would come as the sun grew higher in the sky.

Starting at the Creek with Willows we explored south following the movement of the river. The water was cool and the morning perfect. As we rounded a corner, we stumbled upon two men fly fishing. Their strong bodies and graceful movements reminded me of how the Old Man must have looked in his younger days.

We continued our walk along the river. When we arrived at the old bridge, I knew I was too tired to backtrack up the river. I spotted the old store and told my husband we could ask someone there for a ride back to Willow Creek.[24] Although he was hesitant about asking for a ride, I told him we would have to get a ride, or he could carry me back. A ride it would be!

The old general store was brimming with camping supplies and treasures. I told the man inside about our predicament. He asked me to wait outside and he would help us.

As we sat on the bench outside the store, I noticed the astounding number of Hummingbirds at the feeders. It was a menagerie of colors bustling around the sweet water. I had never seen so many in one place! I was mesmerized by their seemingly frantic movements.

Before long, the man came out and requested us to get into his truck. Our short ride to the Creek with Willows was filled with his stories about his general store and the surrounding wilderness. This man delighted us as our short ride came to end. We thanked him for his assistance.

On the ride home I thought about our day at the river. The Old Man had said in his 📖, "It is well said that 'God subtracts from the allotted time of man, those hours spent fishing.'"[25] I think spending time at a river counts too.

PART III – The Oasis

The Dream
The Life-Giving River
The Butterfly Maiden
The Trickster Coyote
Mr. Jack Rabbit
Butterflies Galore
Mommy & Baby Cow
A Rafter of Wild Turkeys
The Cow in the Mud
The Shadow
The Two Knolls
My Special Butterfly
The Thunder of Wind
Sparkling Spider Webs
Snowy Winter

The Dream

After spending two years searching for the in the northern mountains, I needed inspiration to continue this journey. I decided I would ask for a night dream to inspire me on where to begin. I knew a lot about the treasure hunt, the Old Man's Poem, and had various ideas and locations for "where warm water halts." I wanted a definite starting point. So that night I asked

The Great Spirit

to send me a dream.

When I awoke in the morning, I thought about the dream. I had dreamt of a large volcano. The image was quite clear: a volcano spewing molten lava and ash. Now there are many volcanoes in the world, but the closest one to me was the volcano in the Sacred Mountains.[26] I knew this volcano had blown its top off millions of years ago and created a huge crater known as the Great Depression.[27]

I studied the Great Depression in detail. I bought maps of the area and learned about the various resurgent domes within the valley. I learned about its streams, its mountains on the rim, and the pueblo next to it.

Stillpoint (Center of All Sacredness) Mountain intrigued me.[28] It lay on the North East rim of the great depression. The River of Bears begins on the north slope of Stillpoint Mountain.[29] This river then travels in a northeasterly direction through the Sacred Mountains. I discovered that the River of Bears is a permanent stream fed by snow melt, rainfall, and the many springs in the Sacred Mountains.

Through my dream of the volcano, I understood the meaning of the first few clues in the riddle ...

My dream had led me to the path towards the .

The Life-Giving River

I had found the life-giving river, but where should I start looking? I traveled out to the River of Bears numerous times looking for clues to the . The river was long and winding. It had supported the lives of the Ancient Ones. I knew there was no way to find the exact spot without more inspiration or good ole Irish Luck .

I always believed the Old Man had acquired the land where he hid the treasure. He could not hide it on Forest Lands owned by someone else. It had to be on his property.

I had gazed along the River of Bears via the great Observatory many, many times, but could not determine what was private property and what was not.[30] However, with the help of knowledge, intuition, and luck, I finally found the Old Man's Land. I could not completely verify it was his land, but I knew it was!

The Old Man had loved this piece of paradise. "How special those hours were, spent watching the waters deepen into cobalt as the flow slowly bent around a bank."[31]

I would travel to this piece of land numerous times over the next five years. I referred to it as the "Oasis." My children accompanied me on many of these trips. My daughter especially loved this place and thought it was a great place for hikes. I met many creatures and learned so many life lessons during my many adventures there including what the Old Man had reminded me so many times:

"God will forgive me, that's what he does."[32]

forgiveness

The Butterfly Maiden

The butterfly maiden appeared in a vision. She rose from the roots of the cottonwood along the bank. I knelt before her asking for her wisdom. She offered me balance, freedom, and nature in the form of rainwater, butterflies, and seedlings. I danced in her presence as she blessed me. The Butterfly Alley was her domain and she cared for all who journeyed along it.

She became my Guardian at the Oasis, watching over me, protecting me, guiding me, loving me.

The Trickster Coyote

One day while resting with my younger son under a small grove of tall Ponderosa it hit me. The Old Man had a secret language, and he was using it to communicate to me. He would take a sentence, rearrange the letters to create a new sentence. It was not an easy secret language to decode.

He was sending messages through cyberspace for all to see, but few to understand. The Old Man, who had now become the Trickster Coyote, would send messages that could be rearranged in several ways. One never knew if the new sentence was correct or not. The Trickster Coyote at his best.

Mr. Jack Rabbit

While driving to the Oasis one day, a large hare startled me and my horse, Bandit. We stopped suddenly and looked at the Great Hare. He told us, "Your quick wit and creative skills will aid you in this journey. Believe in yourself and you will continue to find innovative ways to solve your great puzzle."

Then he jumped away. His large ears turning back towards us to listen for our departure. I sat there for a moment contemplating his wise words.

Butterflies Galore

One spring day while crossing the River of Bears a flutter of butterflies arose from the water right in front of Bandit and me. It was a beautiful bouquet of butterflies. The graceful, two-tailed swallowtails flitted away. Their graceful fluttering was magical. One came back and landed on my shoulder. I listened to her quiet whisper.

"I am the joy you seek, the spiritual rebirth you pursue, the hope you cradle each day. Embrace all the changes that are coming to your life."

Mommy & baby Cow

While enjoying the warmth of the sun after looking for the , my little guy and I laid by the babbling brook and rested. Out of the quiet we heard the moo of a young calf. He was looking for his mother. He called for her again and she responded. The call and response continued until the little one was close by his momma.

My little guy called for me and smiled. I went to him and we cuddled by the water.

A Rafter of Wild Turkeys

The sandy road to the Oasis meandered for over many miles through the Sacred Mountains. One day I encountered a rafter of over fifty wild turkeys. It was the first time I had ever seen wild turkeys. They ran across the dirt road and then "flew" to their resting place. It happened so fast, but their majesty was apparent.

 reminded me that the turkey spirit animal is a symbol of abundance. They bring the message of unlocking the richness of one's life so that one can appreciate everything.

The Cow in the Mud

The Old Man had said one time, "Until you have loved a cow, part of your soul remains undiscovered."[33] I learned that lesson one day while riding Bandit home. It was late in the afternoon and dark clouds were approaching. I noticed vultures circling up in the sky. Hmmm ....

They must have their eye on something. I discovered that it was a magnificent cow stuck in the mud. I tied Bandit to a tree and raced over to the cow. He was stuck in the mud up to its chest. He looked at me with sad eyes knowing that he was doomed without my help. I now knew what it was to love a cow – even though I had just met him.

I noticed coyote footprints near the poor cow. There was no way for me to rescue the cow by myself. I left it but found the owners of it by its tag. I left a note scratched on paper on their door and hoped for the best.

This cow stayed in my mind until my next visit when I saw he had been rescued. The mud had been removed and the cow was nowhere to be seen. My efforts had helped to save him.

The sacred cow became a reminder to me of Mother Earth and all she gives to us. Mother Earth nurtures us throughout our life. The cow has given us life through milk and meat.

The Shadow

The Shadow would creep up behind me when I least expected. It would place doubt within my heart – sending me spiraling downwards. It would laugh at me for searching for "treasure." It would tell me that I was wasting my time. It would tell me that I needed to reevaluate my life. It would laugh, laugh, and laugh. It did not know the true reasons for my journey. It told me that my treasure hunting was absurd, pointless, useless, unproductive, and futile. It did not know what was in my heart and soul.

It would come to me on many occasions, trying to stop me from my journey. It came in the forms of other people and through my own mind. It was debilitating at times, but I continued.

The Two Knolls

The double omega intrigued all who knew about it. The Old Man had given no hints about it. I discovered the meaning of the double omega on one of my adventures to the Oasis.

There were two knolls at the Oasis which were close to each other. The dry creek separated them. As I gazed at the knolls one day, I immediately saw the two omegas. Each hill was an omega! Yes, I could see it clearly now. No wonder the Old Man loved the omega symbol so much. It was a symbol of his treasured place.

My Special Butterfly

On a crisp, cold winter day I looked atop one of the knolls for the treasure. I was near a young Ponderosa tree moving dirt aside. I was oblivious to all that surrounded me until a glimmering, white butterfly landed on my hand. It stayed with me as I studied it.

My sacred journey was reaffirmed with this butterfly. It reminded me that I was in a season of transformation, growth, and discovering my own truth and inner wisdom. The Old Man had once offered me this guidance, *"No time spent in thought is wasted and nothing is too small to know."*[34]

The Thunder of Wind

I heard the thunder of wind in the Oasis. Let me explain. It was a crisp, winter day and the sky was growing dark. I was atop the second knoll looking down upon the icy waters of the River of Bears. Suddenly the wind came roaring down the canyon. It was loud and moved quickly along the walls. It terrified me. The intense, deafening sound chilled me to the bones. The Old Man had warned me once, "Mountains can suffer instant personality reversals."[35]

This vital breath of the universe, the divine messenger, delivered the reminder of the transient, the elusive and the intangible.

Sparkling Spider Webs

The strings of webs sparkled in the sunlight as I lay beneath the great Douglas Fir. I remembered that webs symbolized the Mother and Divine Feminine. I could see my life's journey on the webs which crossed each other and led to different trees. The web of life symbolized fate and destiny. I knew my journey would take me to new adventures. I needed only to take the leap of faith.

Snowy Winter

The Oasis in winter teemed with birds probing for pinecone seeds and other seeds. The icy waters created sculptures of layers, dams, and walls. The water chilled the fingers of those brave enough to touch it. The sentinel evergreen trees guarded the Oasis. A winter wonderland that inspired me as I gazed at its beauty.

PART IV – Finding the Treasure

The Old Man's Riddle

Understanding the Riddle

Finding the Blaze

The Secret Vault

Devastation

News from the Old Man

More News from the Old Man

The Old Man's Riddle

As I have gone alone in there
And with my treasures bold,
I can keep my secret where,
And hint of riches new and old.

Begin it where warm waters halt
And take it in the canyon down,
Not far, but too far to walk.
Put in below the home of Brown.

From there it's no place for the meek,
The end is ever drawing nigh.
There'll be no paddle up your creek,
Just heavy loads and water high.

If you've been wise and found the blaze,
Look quickly down, your quest to cease,
But tarry scant with marvel gaze,
Just take the chest and go in peace.

So why is it that I must go
And leave my trove for all to seek?
The answer I already know,
I've done it tired, and now I'm weak.

So hear me all and listen good,
Your effort will be worth the cold.
If you are brave and in the wood
I give you title to the gold.[36]

Understanding the Riddle

Stanza 1 (No Clues)

As I have gone alone in there
And with my treasures bold,
I can keep my secret where,
And hint of riches new and old.

Stanza 2 (Four Clues)

Begin it where warm waters halt
(Clue 1: The Great Depression)
And take it in the canyon down,
(Clue 2: Down Stillpoint Mountain)
Not far, but too far to walk.
(Clue 3: Walk along the River of Bears)
Put in below the home of Brown.
(Clue 4: Beneath the Ancient Ones' home)

Stanza 3 (Four Clues)

From there it's no place for the meek,
(Clue 5: The place is on the River of Bears)
The end is ever drawing nigh.
(Clue 6: The river takes a sharp left near the place)
There'll be no paddle up your creek,
(Clue 7: A dry creek is between the two knolls)
Just heavy loads and water high.
(Clue 8: The creek is filled with big rocks
where water used to flow)

Stanza 4 (One Clue)

If you've been wise and found the blaze,
(Clue 9: The blaze found in nature)
Look quickly down, your quest to cease,
But tarry scant with marvel gaze,
Just take the chest and go in peace.

Stanza 5 (No Clues)

So why is it that I must go
And leave my trove for all to seek?
The answer I already know,
I've done it tired, and now I'm weak.

Stanza 6 (No Clues)

So hear me all and listen good,
Your effort will be worth the cold.
If you are brave and in the wood
I give you title to the gold.

Finding the Blaze!

It took me many years in the Oasis to find the blaze. It was not inherently obvious. In fact, it took a "first blaze" of hidden secret letters in nature to find the "final Blaze". I finally discovered it one day while trying to think in a new, different way.

The BLAZE, in a word, was "OWL."

The Secret Vault

Next I needed to find the final resting place of the chest. I knew every inch of the Oasis. It was the end of May in 2020 and unusually hot. Too hot for either Bandit or me to head out to the Oasis. I continued to think, however, about the secret vault. Suddenly one day I figured out a couple of prime locations! Eureka! I wrote the Old Man and told him of the discovery in my mind.

Devastation

Two days later, on June 6, 2020, the Old Man told the world that the chest had been found. I was confused. Did he mean me? I wrote asking him. No response. No photos of the chest. I wrote him several times, no response.

NO, NO, NO ......

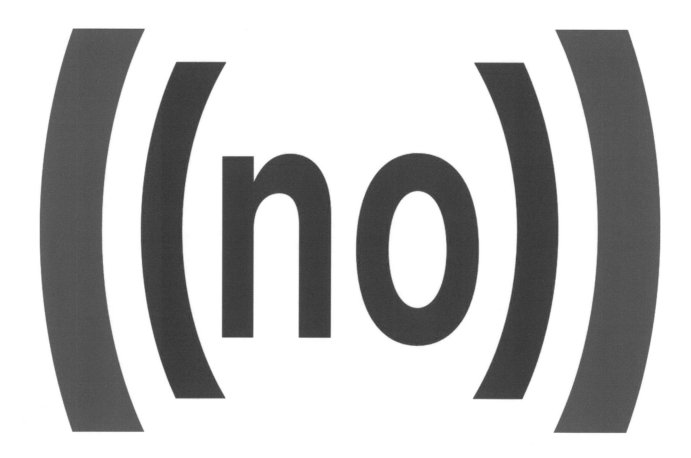

News from the Old Man

THE TREASURE HAS BEEN FOUND

It was under a canopy of stars in the lush, forested vegetation of the Rocky Mountains and had not moved from the spot where I hid it more than 10 years ago. I do not know the person who found it, but the poem in my book led him to the precise spot.

I congratulate the thousands of people who participated in the search and hope they will continue to be drawn by the promise of other discoveries.

So the search is over. Look for more information and photos in the coming days. f[37]

SHOCK, CONFUSION

WHAT NOW?

More News from the Old Man

The treasure chest was found by a man I did not know and had not communicated with since 2018.

Photo of the Chest taken
not long after it was discovered.

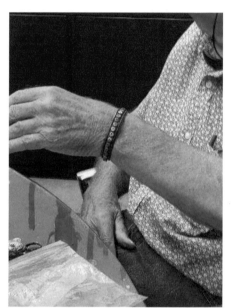

The bracelet on my arm
was wet when found. The
silver tarnished black.

Removing objects from the Chest. It is darker than it was ten years ago when I left it on the ground and walked away.

The finder wants me to remain silent and I always said the finder gets to make those two calls. Who and where. f 38

DISBELIEF, CONFUSION, DENIAL

PART V – The Journey Back Home

The Road Back

Returning to the Ordinary World

Treasures in my own Backyard

Sharing the Gift

The Road Back

The road back home was long and lonely. I started back home on the summer solstice. Bandit and I walked slowly. Time was all we had.

The journey had not ended like it was supposed to. I was the one who was destined to find the treasure.

I had found the blaze and was close to finding the secret vault. But the 🎁 had been grabbed from underneath me.

As we traveled home, I remembered all the adventures I had along the journey. I vacillated between drowning in depression and looking for meaning. Even though beauty surrounded me, I could not see it.

And then ...

the Old Man died.

I could not believe that he was gone.

Returning to the Ordinary World

Returning to the Ordinary World was not easy. There was no comfort, there was no happiness, there was no joy.

The days were long without the hope of adventure. No one really understood my sorrow. No one understood that my dreams had been crushed.

Treasures in my own Backyard

"So now I sit here past midnight, beside my juniper fire, reflecting back to the year when my awareness took its first steps."[39]

It was not until the Winter Solstice arrived that I began to feel a little better. I realized my **Sacred Quest** had not been in vain. I had experienced so much spiritual growth, had so many exciting adventures, and met many Spirit Animals who had taught me so much. Slowly I began to appreciate the treasures I had received. And there were so many.

I had found exciting places to visit. I knew the Oasis like no other person. I had met so many intriguing characters along the way. And I had known and understood the Old Man in a way that only a few had known.

Sharing the Gift

On the Feast of Epiphany 2021, I had, well, my own Epiphany! I had been on a true hero's journey.

I had received the Call to Adventure and Crossed the Threshold. The tests were passed by experiencing the Adventures and listening to what surrounded me. The Ordeal was unraveling the Old Man's Riddle and heeding the words of the Spirit Animals. Refusing to give in to Doubt allowed me to finish the Quest. My reward, however, would not be realized until I had finished the journey back home.

The Hero`s Journey

Every true Hero's Journey includes a Gift received. The Old Man had shared with me the gift he had received on his own journey: a realization –

"When this realization hit me, at last I knew. If I cannot enrich those with whom I interact each day and cause them to be better for my having passed their view, then I have wasted my turn. That I succeed in this endeavor is not as important as it is for me to make a solid try. For if the try is sincere I have succeeded in whatever failure resulted. ... I have finally found my way and am at peace with all of it."[40]

After reaching home and living the Ordinary Life again, I realized that the gift that permeated my entire journey was:

The Sacrament of the Present Moment

I had received the gift many times on the journey ... during all the Adventures, finding the Oasis, listening to the Sacred Animal Spirits. It was there all along. The calling of the mountains and the forests aided me in slowing down my mind and living in the moment. "It's the being there, in the tranquility and silence of one's self ...," the Old Man had told me.[41]

It is a rare gift to live in the moment, not thinking of the past or the future. Only the present. I finally had my response for one of life's great questions – How do we achieve inner peace?

My answer –

To experience the Present Moment and all it has to offer.

I knew I had to share
this realization with others.

Moon Shadow and the Old Man

Moon Shadow and her Mentor
on his 89th Birthday

TREASURE

ACKNOWLEDGMENTS

A sincere remembrance and thanks to Forrest Fenn who created the Treasure Hunt. He graciously gave all of us a chance to find a million dollar treasure. Likewise, he shared his precious time with treasure hunters at his home and around Santa Fe. You will live in my heart forever.

A big thank you to Dal Neitzel who created a blog for treasure hunters to share their stories, receive new stories from Forrest, and have fun contests. It was through the blog that I learned so much about Forrest. Although the blog has been closed, you can still find Dal at dalneitzel.com.

To my husband, John, who has always supported me in my endeavors. He graciously gives his time and energy to assist me. He is the one with whom I enjoy living in the present moment.

To my children, Matthew, Joshua, and Alejandra, you are the true joy that permeates my life. Thank you for accompanying me on this adventure. You bless me every day with your presence.

To my beloved friend, Acacia McCombs, with whom I have had the privilege to enjoy many long, meaningful conversations, your friendship is a blessing. Acacia is the one who first suggested that I was on a Hero's Journey.

I am forever grateful for my dear friend, Hope B. DuBois, who assisted in editing my book. She provided insightful critiques, corrections, and encouragement. We have embarked on several adventures together over the years. She has remained a faithful and true friend to me for 20+ years.

To my inner circle of friends who read my initial draft and encouraged me to pursue writing a book, I owe you a debt of gratitude.

A special thanks to some of my favorite fellow Treasure Hunters whom I met along the way – Cynthia M., Jamie and Bill, and Slurbs. Thank you for your kindness and for sharing your own journey with me.

Finally, a loving thank-you to my furry friends who kept me company while I wrote: Sparky, Sassy, Scotty, and Cosmo. You are my pack.

BOOK GROUP QUESTIONS

PART I

- Do you think Moon Shadow knew she was beginning a Hero's Journey?
- To what adventure have you been called?
- What is keeping you from accepting the challenge?
- Who is your mentor? Who are your allies?

PART II

- What propelled Moon Shadow to continue searching for the treasure? How did she determine where her next adventure would be?
- When have you encountered adventures? What were they? Travel, friendships, life experiences?
- Who has accompanied you on your adventures?

PART III

- Why did Moon Shadow label her search area as an oasis? Who was her guardian?
- Where have you found an oasis? Which Spirit Animals have come to you in your oasis?

- Which people in your life would you invite to come into your oasis with you? Who would you not invite?

PART IV

- How did Moon Shadow solve the riddle? Do you think she solved it correctly? If not, why?
- What riddles or puzzles have you had to solve in your own life?
- If something does not work out the way you wanted, how do you react?

PART V

- How does Moon Shadow react to her failure of finding Fenn's treasure? Do you think other adventures lie ahead for Moon Shadow?
- How do you react when you fail to reach a goal? Are failed goals without merit?
- Is it necessary to look for sacred quests? Or do sacred quests find you?

END NOTES

PART I

[1] Forrest Fenn on the Today Show

[2] Forrest Fenn, *The Thrill of the Chase (TTOTC)* (Santa Fe, NM One Horse Land & Cattle Co. 2010), 131

[3] Ibid.

[4] The United States Air Force

[5] Forrest Fenn's Office in his Santa Fe, NM home

[6] Fenn, *TTOTC*, 5

[7] Ibid., 14

[8] Ibid., 75

PART II

[9] Battleship Rock, Jemez Springs, NM

[10] Fenn, *TTOTC*, 63

[11] Manby Hot Springs, Taos, NM

[12] Bandit = Honda Pilot

[13] Rio Grande and Long John Dunn Bridge, Arroyo Hondo, NM

[14] Taos, NM

[15] Waterfall in Rio en Medio, large white dog belonging to a nearby resident

[16] Monastery of Christ in the Desert, Abiquiu, NM

[17] Fenn, *TTOTC*, 4

[18] Pecos Wilderness, NM

[19] Pecos River = River of Trading; Willow Creek, Pecos Wilderness, NM

[20] Tererro Mining Camp, Pecos Wilderness, NM

[21] Fenn, *TTOTC*, 147

[22] Cave Creek, Pecos Wilderness, NM

[23] Joseph Campbell

[24] The Tererro General Store, Pecos Wilderness, NM

[25] Fenn, *TTOTC*, 125

PART III

[26] Sacred Mountains = Jemez Mountains, NM

[27] Great Depression = Valles Caldera, NM

[28] Stillpoint Mountain = Chicoma Mountain, NM

[29] River of Bears = Rio del Oso, Jemez Mountains, NM

[30] Google Earth

[31] Fenn, *TTOTC*, 125

[32] Ibid., 138

[33] Ibid., 31

[34] Ibid., 147

[35] Ibid., 63

PART IV

[36] Ibid., 132 (The Riddle/Poem)

[37] From Forrest Fenn on June 6th, 2020 at 8pm PST on dalneitzel.com

[38] Updated June 16th, 2020 By Forrest on dalneitzel.com

PART V

[39] Fenn, *TTOTC*, 15

[40] Ibid., 103

[41] Ibid., 125

IMAGE CREDITS

PART I

*Spiral Symbol: "Rock Art Gila Symbol" by Unknown Author is a Free Photo found at: //openclipart.org/image/2400px/svg_to_png/124603/RockArt-GilaSpiral1.png

*Laundry Pins: "Clothespins / Wäscheklammern I" by manoftaste.de is licensed under CC BY 2.0. To view a copy of this license, visit //creativecommons.org/licenses/by/2.0/

*Treasure Chest: "Treasure chest with gold coins.svg" by Clker-Free-Vector-Images on Pixabay is marked under CC0 1.0. To view the terms, visit //creativecommons.org/publicdomain/zero/1.0/deed.en

*Open Book: "Book" by Unknown Author is a Free Photo found at //cdn.pixabay.com/photo/2013/07/13/10/49/book-157851_640.png

Mentor: "Mentor" by Unknown Author is licensed under Pixabay License, Free for commercial use.

*Hat: "Cowboy Hat" by Unknown Author is found on MSWord/Insert Online Photo and is licensed under CC BY-SA.

Threshold: "Threshold" by Unknown Author is found on MSWord/Insert Online Photo and is licensed under CC BY-SA.

PART II

Battleship Rock: Treasures of Northern New Mexico Series by artist, Elizabeth Schultze

Hot Spring: "Hot Spring" by Unknown Author is found on MSWord/insert Photo and is licensed under CC BY-SA

Artist Village: "Pueblo" by Unknown Author is licensed under Pixabay License - Free for commercial use

Waterfall: "Waterfall near Santa Fe" by Laurie Drake was purchased through iStock: Stock Photo ID: 1199551970

White dog: "Great Pyrenees Mountain Dog" by Unknown Author is a Free Photo found at: //upload.wikimedia.org/wikipedia/commons/thumb/c/c7/Great_Pyrenees_Mountain_Dog.jpg/1200px-Great_Pyrenees_Mountain_Dog.jpg found at: //upload.wikimedia.org/wikipedia/commons/b/b5/MonasteryChristDesert.jpg

Monastery: "Christ in the Desert Monastery" by Unknown Author is a Free Photo found at: //upload.wikimedia.org/wikipedia/commons/b/b5/MonasteryChristDesert.jpg

Gold Frog: "Golden Poison Frog" by Unknown Author is marked under CC0 1.0. To view the terms, visit //creativecommons.org/publicdomain/zero/1.0/

Small Stream: "Small stream" by teteroon is marked under CC0 1.0. To view the terms, visit //creativecommons.org/licenses/cc0/1.0/

Picnic: "Picnic in a park" by Unknown Author is a Free Photo found at: //c.pxhere.com/photos/cf/08/book_picnic_park_summer_reading_nature_picnic_bl anket_pond-1382029.jpg!s

Inside a Cave: "Inside a Cave" by Unknown Author found on MSWord/Insert Online Photo and is licensed under CC BY-SA.

Hummingbird: "507 - BROAD-BILLED HUMMINGBIRD (6-18-09) - (4)" by Sloalan is marked under CC0 1.0. To view the terms, visit //creativecommons.org/licenses/cc0/1.0/

PART III

*The Great Spirit: "Dove" by Unknown Author is a Free Photo found at: //res.publicdomainfiles.com/pdf_view/73/13931787015352.png

Volcano Depression: "Top of Volcano" by Unknown Author found on MSWord/Insert Online Photo and is licensed under CC BY-SA.

Stream in Forest: "Stream: by Unknown Author is a Free Photo by pixabay.com found at: //cdn.pixabay.com/photo/2016/11/28/17/07/stream-1865419_640.jpg

Butterfly Maiden: "Kachina Doll (Pahlikmana)" by Hopi Pueblo is licensed with CC BY 3.0. To view a copy of this license, visit //creativecommons.org/licenses/by/3.0/

Coyote: "Carnivore-Coyote" by Unknown Author is a Free Photo found at: //images.pexels.com/photos/397867/pexels-photo-397867.jpeg?w=1200&h=627&fit=crop&auto=compress&cs=tinysrgb

Jack Rabbit: "Black Tailed Jackrabbit" by Unknown Author is a Free Photo found at: /pixnio.com/free-images/fauna-animals/bunny-rabbit/black-tailed-jackrabbit-animal.jpg

Butterfly: "Butterfly" by Judy Gallagher is a Free Photo found at: //commons.wikimedia.org/w/index.php?curid=54631788

Calf & Cow: "Calf and Cow" by Unknown Author is a Free Photo found at: //www.publicdomainpictures.net/pictures/10000/velka/calf-and-cow-23441282066956XK1H.jpg

Wild Turkey: "Wild Turkeys" by Unknown Author is found on MSWord/Insert Online Photo and is licensed under CC BY-SA

COW: "Cow/Steer/Cattle" by Unknown Author is a Free Photo found at: //cdn.pixabay.com/photo/2015/08/20/15/03/cow-897533_640.jpg

Question Mark: "ketidakpastian" by Unknown Author is marked under CC0 1.0. To view the terms, visit https://creativecommons.org/licenses/cc0/1.0/

Omega Symbol: "Black Omega Symbol" by Unknown Author is a Free Photo found at: //www.publicdomainpictures.net/pictures/60000/velka/black-omega-symbol.jpg

Butterfly on Hand: "Butterfly" by Unknown Author is a Free Photo found at: i1.pickpik.com/photos/722/39/629/butterfly-dovetail-hand-colorful-preview.jpg

Wind: "Wind" by Unknown Author is found on MSWord/Insert Online Photo and is licensed under CC BY-SA

Spiderweb: "Spiderweb" by Unknown Author is a Free Photo found at: //upload.wikimedia.org/wikipedia/commons/a/a2/Spiderweb.jpg

Winter Stream: Stream Waterfall winter free photo : /upload.wikimedia.org/wikipedia/commons/7/7c/Stream-waterfall-winter_-_West_Virginia_-_ForestWander.jpg

PART IV

Great Horned Owl: "Great Horned Owl" by Andy Morffew is a Free Photo found at: //upload.wikimedia.org/wikipedia/commons/f/f0/Great_Horned_Owl%2C_Venice%2C_Florida_1.jpg

Vault: "Vault" by Unknown Author is found on MSWord/Insert Online Photo and is licensed under CC BY-SA

NO: "NO" by Unknown Author is a Free Photo found at: //upload.wikimedia.org/wikipedia/commons/thumb/8/8f/ISO_639_Icon_no.svg/1024px-ISO_639_Icon_no.svg.png

PART V

Mountain Path: "Mountain path" by Unknown Author is a Free Photo found at: //pxhere.com/en/photo/695794

Mountain with clouds: "Mountain with Clouds" by Unknown Author is found on MSWord/Insert Online Photo and is licensed under CC BY-SA

Maze: "Maze" by Unknown Author is found on MSWord/Insert Online Photo and is licensed under CC BY-SA

Hero's Journey: "Hero's Journey" by Unknown Author is a Free Photo found at: //upload.wikimedia.org/wikipedia/commons/6/61/Hero´s_Journey.jpg

Gift Box: "Gift Box" by Unknown Author is found on MSWord/Insert Online Photo and is licensed under CC BY-SA

Forget Me Nots: "Forget Me Nots" by Unknown Author is found on MSWord/Insert Online Photo and is licensed under CC BY-SA

Other Photos

Moon Shadow and Old Man: Photo property of Elizabeth Schultze

Moon Shadow and her Mentor on his 89th Birthday: Photo property of Elizabeth Schultze

*Designates symbol used in more than one place

REFERENCES

Fenn, Forrest. *The Thrill of the Chase – A Memoir*. One Horse Land & Cattle
Co. 2010.

CPSIA information can be obtained
at www.ICGtesting.com
Printed in the USA
BVHW022229270421
605942BV00008B/215